Contents

Preface

Exercises and Activities for Twos, Threes, and Fours is the second volume in the Moving and Growing series published jointly by the Canadian Institute of Child Health and Fitness Canada. Both these institutions strongly endorse the promotion of physical activity for small children. What's more, they encourage parents and caregivers to participate with their children and to savour the joy of their moving, growing, learning, and loving.

The original manuscript was written by Dr. M.L. Dalley. Dr. Dalley is a writer consultant on elementary and nursery school motor development programs and part time lecturer at the University of Ottawa, Ottawa, Ontario. Terri Winik prepared the illustrations. To both persons we extend our gratitude for their expertise. Special mention is also due to the Advisory Committee, a group of volunteers experienced in the field of motor development of young children:

Barbara Amundrud
Colleen Martin
Wendy Murray
Ellen Richardson.

Further copies of Exercises and Activities for the First Two Years and this volume of Moving and Growing series are available from:

Canadian Institute of Child Health
17 York Street
Ottawa, Ontario
K1N 5S7
(613) 238-8425

Moving and Growing

Exercises and Activities for Twos, Threes, and Fours

The original manuscript was written by
Dr. Marlene Dalley

Illustrations by Terry Winik

Produced by Fitness Canada and the
Canadian Institute of Child Health

Également disponible en français sous le titre
« Mouvement et Croissance »

This booklet is the second in the *Moving and Growing* series.
The first booklet, *Exercises and Activities for the First Two Years*, and this booklet are available from:

> The Canadian Institute of Child Health
> 17 York Street
> Ottawa, Ontario
> K1N 5S7
> (613) 238-8425

Throughout the text of Moving and Growing we have equally used "he" and "she" when referring to the child. This was done deliberately in accordance with affirmative action guidelines and with the conviction that "he/she" lent to very awkward reading.

The production of this booklet was made possible by a contribution from Fitness Canada.

ISBN 0-919747-10-8

Introduction

Children enjoy moving as much as they need to move. They are so busy and active that adults often envy their energy. Characteristically, children of two, three, and four are healthy and physically fit. Moving from dawn to dusk is their source of joy, self expression, creativity, and learning. To them the world is a playground and objects are toys. Is it any wonder that they are often "into everything?" Do not despair. They are growing and learning as they move through their daily activities.

Since children in this age group want to please others, it is important that parents, siblings, grandparents, and caregivers participate in their activities. Playing and exercising together allows an adult to show interest, approval, and acceptance. Occasionally, they may ignore you or spend time showing off. But, be patient; they need you nearby to reassure, praise, and encourage them.

Exercises and Activities for Twos, Threes, and Fours is designed primarily to provide parents or any other person involved in caring for a child of two to four with information about activities to enhance physical fitness and motor skill development. The activities may also be adapted for use in day care centres, nursery schools, and other group settings.

Activities for each age group are presented separately so that the "you and me" exercises, motor development activities, and games you select are appropriate for the age group of your child.

As you prepare to use this volume which is designed to assist you in planning interesting and enjoyable physical activities, several important factors should be kept in mind. First, although all children follow a basic development pattern, children grow and develop at widely varying paces. The movement abilities listed for each age group are only general guidelines for observing development. It is important to follow your child's pace and not to make comparisons with other children.

Second, activities that stimulate one child may not interest another. Try an activity with your child in a relaxed and reassuring way. If he responds by laughing and smiling or is clearly having fun, continue on. If not, stop and try that activity again some other time.

Third, by the age of two, your child has developed and refined a number of basic movement skills. As you plan and implement your child's activity program, you should remember that motor skills are categorized according to the benefits derived from them: they may increase body awareness, spatial awareness, locomotor skills, nonlocomotor skills, and manipulative skills. Each of these benefits is extremely important for several reasons.

Body awareness is crucial to the development of a child's view of "self" thus influencing his willingness to participate in physical activities. Identification of body parts and differentiation of the right and left sides of the body increase body awareness.

Spatial awareness assists the child in orientating his body to the surroundings, so he can skillfully move in relation to objects and persons. As spatial awareness improves a child will manage different levels, sizes, shapes, directions, and pathways.

Locomotor skills enable a child to move from one place to the other. These motor skills include crawling, walking, running, jumping, hopping, leaping, skipping, sliding, and galloping.

Nonlocomotor skills increase the possibilities for range of movement. These motor skills include actions such as bending and stretching, pushing and pulling, twisting and turning, falling and rising, and swinging and swaying.

Manipulative skills help the child handle and control objects. These motor skills include actions such as rolling, tossing, bouncing, catching, kicking, and striking.

● **Getting Started**

This volume is divided into sections by age level. Each section describes the movement abilities of children at each age and then presents appropriate "you and me" exercises, motor development activities, and games. Each of these groups of activities has specific benefits.

"You and Me" exercises are designed to relax you and your child before and after any activity and improve physical fitness levels by developing cardiorespiratory (heart-lung) endurance, strength, flexibility, agility, speed, power, and balance.

Motor Development Activities can be done at home and in the surrounding environment. They create learning situations to enhance development of awareness and basic movement skills. They improve body and spatial awareness as well as locomotor, and manipulative skills.

Games are used as a tool for developing awareness, basic movement, social skills, and increasing physical fitness levels. They are fun, interesting, challenging, and provide a way for you and your child to enjoy playtime together. The games are classified for use with small or large groups and as either active or passive in nature.

● Why Use Moving and Growing

A child's need to move is very apparent in the preschool years. She is always moving from place to place and toy to toy. Each movement is a channel for self expression, a way of learning and experimenting to find just what she is capable of doing. Often a child's surroundings are so restrictive that they inhibit full exploration and movement. Nor do children always use and develop all their movement skills as they go about their daily activities. Therefore, it is important that a well balanced program of physical activities be planned to enable them to experience many different types of movements in a variety of situations.

● How to Use Moving and Growing

The following procedure is designed to help you plan your child's activities. The program need not be long and complex. Any amount of time set aside to exercise with your child will be fun and rewarding for both of you. Relax, smile, roll together on the floor, and enjoy this special time together.

Warm Up
Select a few relaxation, bending and stretching exercises from the "you and me" exercise section to relax, loosen, and warm up the body in preparation for more strenuous exercises. These exercises also establish the trust that gives the child assurance that the exercises to follow will be fun and worth while.

Physical Fitness
Select a few exercises for development of the arms, legs, back, and abdomen from the "you and me" exercises. Talking, laughing, touching, and loving are important to the success of each exercise.

Skill Development
Introduce a new skill or encourage refinement of a previously learned skill by choosing appropriate motor development activities. Select one or several of the awareness and motor skill activities.

Game
Choose a game that the child enjoys playing. The skills required in a game can reinforce newly introduced actions and skills.

Cool Down
Activity time is a special time for the child. She may be very excited after sharing it with you. Select relaxation exercises that calm and settle your child.

Some "do's" and "don'ts" will assist you as you begin your program.

8

Some Do's

- Dress the child in loose-fitting clothes. If the weather is warm, the fewer clothes the better. Children relax more readily when they wear very little.
- Dress comfortably yourself in loose fitting everyday clothes.
- Let your child go barefoot. If a shoe must be worn, choose a nonslip slipper or sneaker.
- Select a favourite toy for your child. This toy can be useful in relaxing, by drawing attention to a movement or initiating a particular exercise.
- Encourage initiative by choosing interesting and safe toys. Commercial toys are good, but usually children enjoy the things that the parents use; for example, a pot, wooden spoon, potato masher, plastic container, or other household item.
- Exercise on a mat or carpet.
- Be totally committed to your child and this exercise session. If you are jumping up and down to answer the telephone or to do something else, the child will feel tense and much of the value of exercising will be lost.
- Adapt the time of exercising and type of exercises to the tempo of the day. It is useless to try to exercise and bake. It is also useless to try and exercise if your child is tired, hungry, and/or generally cranky. You and your child must both demonstrate a willingness to share this experience fully. A good suggestion is to play a favourite record to set a relaxing atmosphere throughout the activity session.
- Begin each exercise by talking and hugging. Build trust based on reassurance and enjoyment.
- Select exercises at the beginning of each session to relax your child. Progress *slowly*, gradually introducing some of the more vigorous exercises at opportune times.
- Listen to your child, noting behaviour and gestures. The child knows her abilities best and will indicate when she is ready to stop and exercise.
- Encourage the timid and/or lazy child. Some children need more encouragement than others.
- Most of all, smile, cuddle, and have fun.

Some Dont's

- Don't force your child or child's body. If there is evidence of resistance, try again another day.
- Don't tire your child. Do one or two exercises and if she is having fun, then continue. If not, try another approach. If this approach fails, try some other time or another day.
- Don't compare the accomplishments of your child with another child's abilities. Each child is unique and will progress at her own pace.

The
Two
Year
Old

The first two years of your child's life have passed and he has spent considerable time exploring the environment, moving and growing. These years were characterized by the rapid development and refinement of a vast repertoire of motor skills. Quickly your child became very skilled at reaching, grasping, manipulating, sitting, crawling, climbing, walking, and running.

During the year between two and three a child's body proportions change considerably as he begins to look more like a child and less like a baby. At the same time play activities change, and your child will begin to imitate your everyday activities around the home. Children of this age especially enjoy pretending to mow the lawn, wash dishes, grocery shop, answer the telephone, and have a tea party.

A child's vast array of acquired skills makes supervision so time consuming and difficult that many refer to this age as the "terrible twos." Despite the demands, most parents cannot help but marvel at the growth and development progress of their child. The tiny infant that formerly lay helpless is now a busy moving child, skillfully climbing to reach for a favourite cookie. This rapid physical development and demonstrated surge of independence can be of concern to any parent or caregiver. However, movement and experimentation are a natural, normal, and necessary element of development of the "terrific twos."

The following hints for parents and caregivers may help them to manage the daily activities of children in this age group.
○ Childproof your home. Place chemicals, dangerous drugs, and harmful objects out of reach. Place a firmly fixed barrier across the top and bottom of a stairwell. Plug electrical outlets with plastic childproof covers. Secure cupboards with special childproof closures. Lock doors so the child cannot wander out of the house alone. Place expensive, treasured, or breakable items away for a few months.
○ Give your child an area or part of an area that is exclusively his. For example, empty a low drawer in the kitchen, make his bedroom or playroom an interesting safe play area, purchase child-sized furniture to accommodate his play needs, place all playthings in a box or laundry basket, and cover the play area with newspaper or cut open plastic garbage bags for messy activities (play dough, painting, water play).
○ Encourage your child to explore, fostering his curiosity with your approval.

A Two's Movement Abilities

The following abilities are presented as guidelines for helping you determine the activities appropriate for this age group.

● Reaching, Grasping, Releasing, and Manipulating

Your two year old
○ strings large beads, spools, and other suitable objects on a boot lace;

- stacks blocks, cans, boxes, ice cream containers, and similar objects or builds simple structures with blocks and objects of various sizes and dimensions;
- throws a ball or bean bag using two hands;
- kicks a large ball without losing balance, or runs after it and stops it with two hands before kicking again;
- hits a suspended balloon, yarn ball, or ball with one or two hands or with a large bat.

● Sitting

Your two year old
- sits with balance on a swing, while being gently pushed from behind by an adult;
- alternates between sitting and standing, while playing with more strength and balance;
- sits on and skilfully moves a riding toy, with a two foot pushing action.

● Crawling and Climbing

Your two year old
- crawls and climbs with a good grip, arm and leg strength, and balance "on" and "off", "over" and "under", and "through" a climbing apparatus and household furniture.

11

● Walking and Running

Your two year old
○ walks forward and backward;
○ walks up and down stairs without help;
○ walks along a board or balance beam with or without help;
○ runs with more control and balance, though he may occasionally lose balance and fall forward.

● Jumping and Landing

Your two year old
○ jumps over a shoe box, carpet square, and/or lines drawn on floor with masking tape;
○ jumps off low stools or steps;
○ lands with alternate feet, straight legs, and a stiff body. Encourage him to land with his ankles flexed, knees bent, and arms outstretched for balance.

● Water Play and Swimming

Almost all twos enjoy
○ playing in the bathtub, child-size pools, and pools, lakes, and rivers with adult support;
○ blowing bubbles in water;
○ kicking their legs and splashing their arms in water with adult support.

You and Me Exercises

Adults are encouraged to exercise with their children when they are very young, as one way of helping them to learn to cooperate. By two years, all children are a bit more independent and will enjoy showing you how well they can perform with none or very little assistance. You can still be actively involved by doing the exercises with or beside your child. Indeed, this is a good time to continue your daily exercise program. The "you and me" exercises suggested here provide an opportunity to play together on a one-to-one basis and to hug and outwardly love your child.

Rocking Together
To relax the body and set a trusting mood.

Position: Snuggle together in a sitting position.

Action: Hold your child while rocking side to side, back and forth.

Wet Dog Shake
To relax all parts of the body.

Position: Any comfortable position.

Action: Pretend you are a wet dog and shake your arms and legs.

Eye Squeeze
To relax the facial muscles.

Position: Lie down on your back and pretend to sleep.

Action: "Sleep" really hard by squeezing your eyes tightly and then relaxing them. Repeat several times.

13

Toe Touches

To stretch the muscles of the arms, back, and legs.

Position: Stand with hands stretched above head.

Action: Bend over and touch toes with knees slightly bent.

Telephone Sit

To stretch the backs of the legs, hip, groin, seat, and abdominal muscles.

Position: Sit with legs extended in front.

Action: Pick up the right foot with right hand and raise it to touch the ear on the same side. The heel of the foot can be a mouthpiece to talk to your favourite person. Repeat on the opposite side.

Sunrise, Sunset

To stretch and strengthen back and legs.

Position: Sit cross-legged with knees bent, hands folded across chest, head between legs.

Action: On cue "the sun rises," slowly unfold your bodies, pushing with hands, gradually rising to standing. Cue "the sun is setting" and reverse action returning to sitting position.

14

Good Morning World!
To strengthen the arms.

Position: Lie flat on your stomachs with your hands on the floor and underneath your shoulders.

Action: Pretend to fall asleep, relaxing with no sound or movement. "Wake up" saying "Good Morning World" by raising your bodies to a semi push-up, keeping your hips, legs, and feet on the floor. Lower your bodies and relax.

Wiggle Toe Sit
To strengthen the abdomen.

Position: Lie flat on your back with your knees bent and feet flat on the floor, hands stretched above head.

Action: Gradually sit up, grasping and wiggling toes. Child says "wiggle, wiggle, wiggle" to show success.

Angry Cat – Happy Dog

To strengthen the abdomen and back.

Position: Kneel on all fours.

Action: Round back up and hiss like an angry cat; sway back, lift head, and wag seat like a happy dog.
Note: Adults should not sway their back as any movement that accentuates the hollow in the lower back can lead to back soreness and strains.

Bouncing Ball

To strengthen knees and thighs.

Position: Child squats down like a ball.

Action: Adult puts gentle but firm pressure on the child's back, making the ball (child) bounce up and down flexing and straightening legs. The amount of pressure determines the amount of bounce.

Dowel, Rod, or Broomlift

To strengthen arms.

Position: Stand facing your child. Take an inverted grip on a rod or dowel. Encourage child to stand and grip rod.

Action: First, lift the child slowly and gently. Hold for two or three seconds, then lower. As the child's weight increases you will need to bend your knees, widen your base, and use the bent to straight leg action to support your child's weight. Second, repeat above action and gently sway the child from side to side, then lower to standing position, watching facial expressions that indicate when he needs to be lowered.

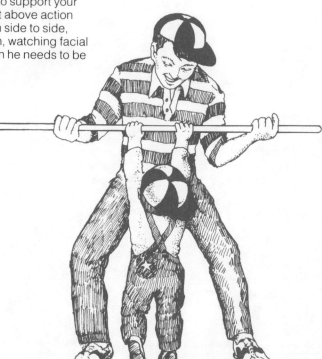

Body Climb
To strengthen legs and arms.

Position: Child and adult stand facing each other.

Action: The adult firmly grasps the child's hands. The child walks up the front part of the adult's legs, tucks knees to chest, turns a somersault, and lands on both feet.

Rock-the-boat
To strengthen back.

Position: Lie flat on your tummies, lifting your arms and legs off floor.

Action: Rock like a boat, forward and backward and side to side. Talk together and make "putt, putt" sounds as you move along in the water.

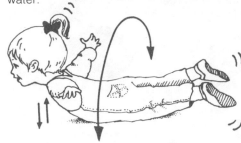

Wheelbarrow

To strengthen arms.

Position: Child lies on stomach, legs straight together with his hands on the floor positioned underneath his shoulders. Stand behind child and firmly support under thighs.

Action: Lift your child until he is balanced on his hands and can walk on them over a short distance.

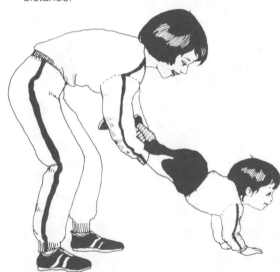

Motor Development Activities

● My Body

To increase body awareness, ask your child to
○ name his body parts;
○ lift, hide, or move different parts of his body; melt like an ice cream cone; pop like popcorn;
○ move body parts in different ways – waving, shaking, swimming, tapping, rubbing, patting, pointing, wiggling, clapping, grasping; for example, swing and sway arms like an elephant's trunk or shake tail like a wet dog;
○ place an object (bean bag, fluff ball, paper ball) between his feet or hands; under his body;
○ Follow actions of the verse "Me"

Me

Two little eyes
That open and close
Two little ears
But just one nose.
Two little shoulders
One on each side.

Two little arms to open wide
Two little hands
Busy all day
Two elbows that bend
They're made that way.

Two little feet so sturdy and strong
And two little legs
That run all day long.

● What Can Body Parts Do?

Have your child stand in front of you and imitate your movements. Select a part of your body to exercise. For example, talk about the actions feet can do: feet can wiggle, curl and stretch, tip toe, stamp, kick, tap, circle, walk, run, hop, skip or, better still, can even dance around the room.

● Action Poems

Have your child perform the movements as directed by these poems. Read the poem aloud, talk about the words and actions, then read again while performing. Memorizing the poem makes it more fun.

> Thumper, bumper,
> Rough and tough,
> Crasher, smasher
> That's enough!
> Lightly, sprightly,
> Soft as mice
> Creeping, sleeping . . .
> That's nice!
>
> Bouncing, bouncing, up and down
> Bouncing, bouncing, turn around
> Bouncing, bouncing, be a clown
> Bouncing, bouncing, hit the ground!

● Over and Under

You can do these activities with your child encouraging, "over" and "under" movements. After your child does the activity, reverse roles. For example,

- Adult lies on floor. Child walks over adult. Reverse roles. Child lies on floor, adult walks over child.
- Adult balances on hands and feet facing floor. Child crawls under bridge made by adult's body. Reverse roles. This is an interesting challenge for the adult. Try your best!

- Adult stands. Child crawls through open legs. Adult's turn!
- Adult sits on floor with legs apart and straight. Child jumps over one leg and then the other leg. Reverse roles.
- Adult holds rod or wooden dowel at a low height. Child jumps or hops over rod. Next!

Explore "over" and "under" by providing ropes, poles, hoops, blankets, and climbing equipment that enable your child to walk, run, climb and jump "over" and "under."

● Zoo Loo

Move your bodies to imitate animals' movements. Musical accompaniment from percussion instruments or records will stimulate you to

- slither along the ground like a snake;
- stomp along like a big black bear;
- hop like a kangaroo that never stops;
- crawl along like a slow old turtle carrying his heavy house on his back;
- fly like a bird so high in the sky;
- climb like a monkey up in a tree;
- gallop like a horse crossing in a field.

● Pathways

Create pathways with obstacles such as cones and chairs that your child can follow by walking, running, or steering a riding toy. Masking tape and rope pathways also provide challenges. Tape a pathway in a straight, angular, or curved pattern. Encourage your child to move, steer a riding toy, or push an object along the selected pathway.

19

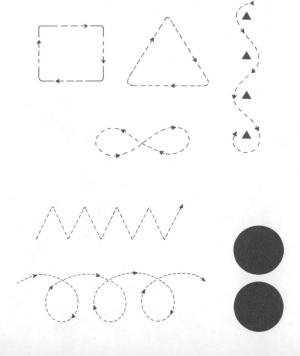

● Stop and Go

Practice starting and stopping while walking and running with your child. Move appropriately to the words "stop" and "go." Later, introduce moving to respond to the crosswalk signs for "stop" and "go." When these activities have been practised, introduce the same concepts while steering a riding toy. This is a very important activity as it teaches your child to respond to your words as well as associate "stop" and "go" with actions. This activity is useful in teaching children street safety.

● Brook Jumps

Create a "brook" with two ropes or masking tape lines. Encourage your child to jump across the "brook" by beginning at the narrow end and gradually moving to jump across the wider end. Landing with alternate feet, straight legs, and a stiff body is characteristic of this age group. Encourage a balanced landing in a crouched position.

● Incline Walk

Have your child walk up and down an incline with support. A wide board, table top, and balance beam can be converted into inclines suitable for walking.

● Ball Play

Select a fairly large (15 cm) soft round ball and encourage your child to touch, hold, and toss it. Then encourage him to throw the ball to you. *Roll* the ball back to the child, since catching is very difficult. If your child appears interested in learning to catch, encourage him to stretch his arms positioned close together out in front of body and keep his eyes on the ball. Gently toss the ball so it lands in his arms. Say "squeeze your ball" so that the child's hands and arms will nestle the ball against his body. Praise and reinforce attempts to catch. As this skill improves, throw a soft ball instructing your child to grasp the ball with his hands.

● Balance Beam

Have your child walk along a sturdy balance beam 10 cm wide and 3 m long and not more than 25 cm off the ground. Some support may be necessary in the beginning. Gradually the child should feel comfortable walking along the board without support. A 2″ × 4″ board stabilized at either end is also suitable for a balance beam.

● Throw and Retrieve

Your child will enjoy throwing and retrieving objects such as a nerf ball, fluff ball, paper ball, or bean bag. Encourage him to experiment by showing you how he can

- ○ throw the bean bag in front of you and go and get it. Repeat;
- ○ throw the bean bag high in the air and go and get it. Repeat. Higher the next time!
- ○ throw the bean bag into a cardboard box 60 cm in front of you;
- ○ throw the bean bag at a large Smiley Face target fixed to the wall. Place the target approximately 60 cm in front of your child and at his height. Your turn next!

● Hitting and Batting

Suspend a ball in a mesh shopping bag at your child's shoulder level. Instruct him to hit the suspended ball with one hand, the other hand, and two hands, until his skill improves and he can hit the ball consistently. Then encourage him to hit the ball with an object such as a large bat or paddle.

● Kicking

Provide your child with a nerf or fluff ball. Encourage him to kick and retrieve it. When he masters this skill and appears balanced, introduce a large playground or beach ball. Kick the ball. Follow its path, stop it with two hands, and kick it again. Try taking turns kicking it!

● Ice Skating

Purchase a pair of ice skates that tightly attach to your child's boots. Place a protective helmet on his head for safety purposes. From behind, support your child under arms, assisting with a gliding motion. If child is not ready for this experience, try again next year.

Water Play and Swimming

Children are not born afraid of water. Their early experiences determine whether water play and swimming will be enjoyable activities for them for the rest of their lives. Parents' attitudes towards water will probably be internalized by the child and that is why every water experience – in the bath, puddle, wading pool, lake, and river – should be a pleasant one. Support your child under the arms while he moves through the water, trickle water over his body, play with water toys, make bubbles in the water, or play splash games to orient your child in the water. So as not to frighten your child, easy splashes, please! You will be able to tell by your child's behaviour and facial expressions which water activities he enjoys and wants to repeat. Provide cheerful and loving support for his efforts.

Water play and swimming with support are important because they accustom your child to water as well as provide opportunities to relax, exercise, and play games. However, the safety of the child at all times is a prime concern. The Canadian Red Cross Society lists the following safety precautions:

- Children love to play in and near water. They must be watched constantly if there are creeks, rivers, or ponds nearby.
- Backyard pools and plastic wading pools *must be* supervised when small children are at play. When there is no supervision, pools should be closed off and plastic wading pools emptied. Remember, a child can drown in three or four inches of water!
- Adequate fencing and locked gates are a *must* for after-hours protection at recreational waterfront areas and pools.
- Watch children whenever they are near water. Small children have drowned in bathtubs, wells, and cesspools when they were left alone for a few minutes.
- Arrange for your children to enroll in classes to learn safe swimming. Make sure that you also know water safety procedures. Remember that young folk move quickly. Watch them at all times!
- After small children learn to swim, they must be supervised at all times.
- Knowing the proper safety procedures is essential. Knowing how to swim is just as important. Parents who do not know how to swim should be encouraged to take lessons with their children.

Rhythm, Music and Dance

Encourage your child to sing and dance. It's fun, healthy, and your child can participate easily. Parents and caregivers must lead the dance or song and your child will imitate your actions. Your child will not judge whether you sing or dance well. Relax, let your body move to the music, sing merrily and you and your child will have a happy time together. It is also fun to pick your child up and dance with him in your arms. Children particularly enjoy turning and spinning. Put on some disco music and see what happens!

Marching Band

Introduce walking and marching to rhythm. Use percussion instruments or bang sticks together, bang the bottom of an old pot, ring a bell, blow a paper towel roll, and shake beans in a jar. Play a child's record and walk and march to the rhythm. Walk and march in straight, angular, and curved pathways, single file or with a partner.

Rhythmical Activities

Using a tambourine or drum, introduce your child to an even rhythm. Walk, run, hop, and jump to the musical accompaniment. Vary tempo. Accent the last note to stop movement.

Singing Rhymes

Wheels on the Bus
The wheels on the bus go round and round
Round and round, round and round
The wheels on the bus go round and round
All day long.

The horn on the bus goes peep, peep,
peep . . .
The wipers on the bus go swish, swish,
swish . . .
The people on the bus bounce up and
down . . .

Mime the actions suggested by the words.

Hop Little Bunnies
See the bunnies sleeping (everyone lies on
the floor with their heads down)
Sleeping, oh so long
Ten o'clock, eleven o'clock
I wonder what is wrong.

They're so still,
Are they ill?

Wake up bunnies! (clap hands)

Hop little bunnies (jump up and start hop-
ping)
Hop, hop, hop.
Hop little bunnies
Hop, hop, hop.
Hop little bunnies,
Hop, hop, hop
All day long.

Games

● Active Games for Two of You

Cookie Monster Tag
The "chase me" game is the forerunner to tag
games. The adult (cookie monster) chases the
child (cookie), then tags or hugs him. The adult
explains how the roles reverse and the game
continues. The most fun of all is when the
game ends with you both in a heap, hugging
and laughing.

Follow the Leader
Enjoy leading your child on an obstacle
course. Walk around the yard, jump over a
stone or pavement crack, crawl under the pic-
nic table, balance on a board, go around a
lawn chair, walk on tip toes, stretch arms to the
sky, take giant steps. Allow your child to be the
leader if he wishes.

Frozen Bean Bags
Balance a bean bag or other suitable object on
your head. Walk around the room. If the bean
bag drops you must stand still and wait for
someone to pick it up and place it back on
your head. Vary tempo and movements.

You and Me Together
Share the experience of walking and running
together. Take a long walk and talk about what
you see and hear. Vary your movements so
you can run like a horse, hop like a bunny,
stamp like an elephant. Moving together is important and fun for you and your child who is
often told "Don't climb up there!" "Don't run!"

Target Game
Purchase a velcro toss game or make your
own by creating an interesting face target on
material velcro sticks to and covering a throwing object with velcro. Throw the object at the
target attached to the wall.

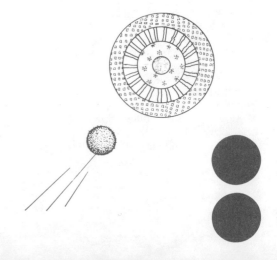

Choo-Choo Train

Stretch two or several ropes lengthwise to make a railway track. Place several cardboard boxes on the ropes to represent box cars. Your child gets into each box and rocks it back and forth, making train sounds. This game can be expanded by having him purchase tickets, providing engineer with a cap, etc.

Hide-and-Seek

Your child will enjoy hiding in many obvious places around the house. Find and hug him. Reverse roles. You will probably need to make sounds to help him find you.

● Passive Games for Two of You

Threading

Threading toys and objects are good to develop hand-eye coordination necessary for the development of life skills. Give your child a piece of string or a boot lace with a good lacing end to thread spools, large noodles, large wooden beads, or wooden blocks with holes. Lacing toys can be purchased in most toy stores.

Building Blocks

Provide the child with boxes, blocks, and cans of various sizes and dimensions for stacking, balancing, and matching to compose a structure. Praise and reinforce attempts to stack objects.

Cover Exploration

Select appropriate containers – plastic storing and cosmetic containers, cleaned detergent bottles, cans with knobbed lids, and pots with lids – for your child to practice removing and replacing covers. Tuck small surprises in the containers (ball, small car, cracker, piece of cheese or fruit, empty spools) to encourage perfection of this skill.

● Active Games for Large Groups

Musical Chairs

Place "child-size" chairs back to back. Have a chair for each child. Children walk in one direction around the outside of the chairs to the rhythm of the music. When the music stops, they sit on the closest chair. Remove a chair each time the music stops and encourage all children to share the few chairs that remain. This game can also be played with carpet squares, pillows, hoops, and adult's knees. Children enjoy playing this game without removing chairs. You may wish to vary movements as they go around the outside of the chairs. Remember, this is the beginning of learning social skills, and children do not readily give up their possessions – even a chair!

The
Three
Year
Old

The three year old has developed a fairly strong awareness of self and is proud of her increasing maturity and ability. Her body is strong and well coordinated, evident when she is walking, running, jumping, and climbing. Her improved coordination and love for adventure indicate readiness for a larger climbing apparatus than was previously suitable. Her attention span has improved considerably, enabling her to explore more possibilities while playing. As your child approaches three and a half years of age, her recent growth may make your child's movements insecure, awkward, or uncoordinated. You need not worry as your child will soon become her coordinated self again.

Interest in riding a tricycle increases. At first, your child will propel the tricycle using a two-foot push against the ground, a skill well perfected on riding toys. Pedalling requires skill and practice, and your child will need a lot of praise and encouragement to master the motion.

The three year old enjoys playing with other children and is now beginning to learn some social skills. But sharing, cooperating, taking turns, accepting rules, being polite, and many other social skills are very difficult for the three year old to learn. Changes in temperament may occur and your child may be described as unmanageable at times. Patience and variety of play situations may be the key to maintaining harmony during this period.

A Three's Movement Abilities

The following abilities are presented as guidelines to help you determine the activities appropriate for this age group.

● Reaching, Grasping, Releasing, and Manipulating

Your three year old
- strings thin laces and threads with firm lacing ends through small objects; for example beads, spools, macaroni, buttons, etc.;
- builds complex structures with building blocks and similar objects of various sizes and dimensions by stacking, interlocking, and balancing them;
- cuts paper with blunt-ended scissors;
- throws a ball to a partner or at a target with some accuracy;
- catches a ball with arms extended stiffly, with occasional success;
- kicks a ball with some accuracy;
- kicks a large ball without loss of balance and retrieves it using two hands while the ball is still in motion;
- hits a suspended ball or punching bag with either or both hands or large bat or paddle;
- hits a ball off a batting tee with a large bat.

● Sitting

A three year old
- sits with strength and balances on a swing or tire swing and begins a rocking pumping action;
- pedals and manœuvres a tricycle or hot wheels.

● Crawling and Climbing

Your three year old
- climbs with coordination, balance and a firm grip on a large climbing apparatus, which provides difficult, varied, and challenging activities.

● Walking and Running

Your three year old
- walks forward and backward at varying speeds and in different directions;
- walks balanced on tip toes;
- walks up and down stairs with more skill, balance, and speed;
- walks skillfully on a balance beam;
- stops and starts on adult's command;
- runs around obstacles;
- runs along different pathways;
- gallops forward.

● Water Play and Swimming

The three year old
- swims moving arms and kicking feet, while firmly supported under hips and chest by adult.

● Jumping and Landing

A three year old
- jumps down from low levels;
- jumps over low barriers, over lines drawn on the floor, and over a rope held at a low level by adults;
- lands with two feet, ankles flexed, knees bent, and arms stretched forward for balance;
- hops with support from an adult.

You and Me Exercises

Lazy-Day Rest
To relax the body.

Position: Lie on your backs on the floor, legs slightly apart, and arms limply at your sides.

Action: Take a deep breath, hold, relax. Pull your toes towards and then away from your bodies, hold, relax. Pull your tummies in, hold, relax. Pull seats together, hold, relax. Make a tight fist with your hands, hold, relax. With your hands at sides, shrug your shoulders, hold, relax. Smile while turning your head from side to side. Frown and repeat action.

Small Ball
To relax the body and stretch muscles.

Position: Kneel on the floor with your legs together.

Action: Rest your seat on your legs, lower your head to the floor, and tuck your hands to your side on floor, pointing backward. Take two or three deep breaths and blow it out. Relax.

Wash the Dishes
To stretch the shoulder muscles.

Position: Stand facing your child, holding her hands.

Action: "Wash the dishes, dry the dishes, turn the dishes over." Swing your arms side to side while singing the rhyme. On the word "over", swing your arms up overhead and turn your child around in a ful circle so your arms are crossed. Repeat arm swings and rhyme and on word "over," return your child to original position (arms uncrossed). Repeat several times.

Angel-in-the-Snow
To stretch the muscles of the arms and legs.

Position: Lie on your backs.

Action: Pretend to be in the snow and move your arms and legs "in" and "out" several times like an angel.
Note: This is a good coordination exercise and excellent lead in to jumping jacks.

Rocking Chair
To strengthen abdomen, legs, and arms and increase balance.

Position: Sit on seats with your legs bent and your hands out to the side for balance.

Action: Tuck your legs into your bodies, wrap your arms around them, feet off the floor and rock forward, backward, side to side.

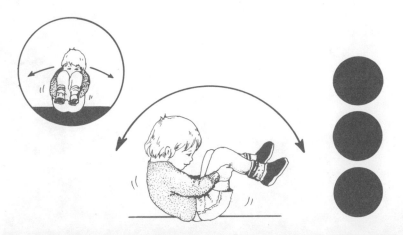

Walk Your Feet
To stretch the back of the legs.

Position: Sit with your knees bent and grasp toes.

Action: Walk forward on your heels until your knees are straight. Continue to grasp your toes and walk back to original position.

Dowel, Rod, or Broom Lift
To strengthen arms.

Position: Stand with bent knees, facing your child. Take an inverted grip on the rod and hold it at arms length.

Action: Your child should grasp the rod firmly as she swings and locks her legs over rod and hangs.

Bridge Over a River
To strengthen hips, buttocks, legs and back.

Position: Lie on your backs with your knees bent and your feet flat on the floor, arms to your sides.

Action: Lift your seats up by balancing on your feet and shoulders. Hold. Pretend a boat is passing under the bridge. Toot! Toot! Relax. Repeat.

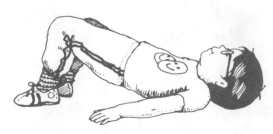

Candle Stand

To stretch the spine and strengthen the muscles of the back, legs, neck, and abdomen.

Position: Lie on your backs with your legs stretched out, your hands close to the side of your bodies with palms facing downward.

Action: With your knees bent, raise your legs high above your heads, hold to the count of 1, 2. Return to lying position. Relax. Repeat. Try some other variations such as moving your legs in a scissor action, crossing legs, touching the floor behind your head with toe of one foot and then the other foot.

Dog Kicks

To strengthen legs.

Position: Hold fluff ball or balloon to the side of your child within kicking distance. Child kneels on all fours.

Action: Encourage your child to kick the ball with a sideward kicking action. Repeat several times on both sides.

Leg Raises

To stretch the leg and groin muscles.

Position: Lie on your sides, one arm underneath and stretched above head, the other hand on the floor in front of the chest to maintain balance.

Action: Raise your leg up, "pointing to the sky" and then lower, resting on the other leg. Repeat several times on this side. Turn over the other side. Repeat exercise several times.

Leg Stretches

To stretch the back of legs.

Position: Sit comfortably on the floor with your legs in front of you.

Action: Grasp your right leg under your knee with your right hand and under your ankle with your left hand and gently straighten leg. Repeat with opposite leg.

This can also be done by sitting behind your child. Place one hand under your child's calf and one hand on top of her knee. Gently, without force, press on the knee, trying to straighten her leg.

Note: This is a good stretching exercise for adults too, although difficult to complete.

Jack-in-the-Box

To strengthen legs and increase muscular and cardiorespiratory endurance.

Position: Squat down with your hands on the floor beside your legs.

Action: Suddenly, jump up and reach as high as possible. Encourage your child to land on the balls of her feet, bending ankles, knees, and hips to return to squatting position. Repeat action several times and rhythmically.

Forward Roll

To stretch muscles and increase coordination.

Position: Your child squats down on a mat or soft surface with her arms on outside of legs and hands placed on the mat in front of her. Lower her head so that her chin touches her chest, making her body very round. Hint: Ask child to hold a fluff ball under chin during whole roll to ensure that her chin is on chest and back is round for rolling.

Action: Roll forward to sitting position.

Assist: Adult guides child through action by kneeling at her side, placing one hand on her back and one hand on the back of her head to keep it tucked. Guide the child's movement with your hands.

Backward Roll

To stretch muscles and increase coordination.

Position: Your child squats down on a mat or soft surface with her back towards the mat and places hands behind her head with thumbs near the ears. Tuck chin to chest and bend head forward making body into round ball.

Action: Roll backward keeping body tucked. Finish in squat or kneeling position. This action is difficult and your child may not stay in the rounded position, stopping her action.

Assist: Guide your child through this action by grasping her hips. As her hips roll upward *lift* them so she can push off with her hands and roll over. Never push child backwards in back rolls as it is too stressful for child's neck. Instead lift her hips.

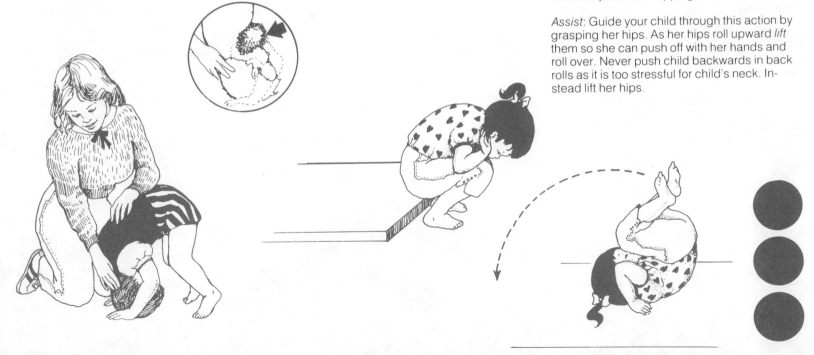

Angry Cat – Happy Dog
To strengthen the abdomen and back.

Position: Kneel on all fours.

Action: Round your backs up and hiss like an angry cat, lift your heads and wag your seats like a happy dog.
Note: Adults should not sway their backs as any movement that accentuates the hollow in the lower back can lead to back soreness and strains.

Wiggle-Toe Sit
To strengthen the abdomen.

Position: Lie flat on your backs with your knees bent and feet flat on floor, hands stretched above head.

Action: Gradually sit up, grasp, and wiggle your toes, saying "wiggle, wiggle, wiggle, wiggle" to show success.

Motor Development Activities

● **My Body**

Increase body awareness by asking your child to show you how she can
- lift, stretch, bend, and/or hide different parts of her body in different ways;
- clap hands rhythmically, varying tempo and pattern;
- swing and sway arms in a variety of ways;
- twist like gum;
- turn like the wheels on a tricycle;
- push and pull on a blanket, towel, or rope;
- hammer a nail;
- saw a board.

Differentiate between the two sides of her body by identifying the parts on the right and left sides. For example, lift your right hand, shake your right hand, touch your foot with your right hand, touch other parts of your body with your right hand.

Repeat activities using the left side.
Note: It helps to place a sock on your child's right hand or a happy face on her right toe, or a sticker on her right knee, etc. Parent or adult should sit *beside* child.

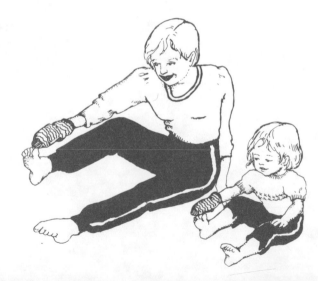

34

● Walking and Running

Enjoy walking and running in different ways together; for example, walk
- imitating animals;
- forward, backward, sideward. To teach the sideward movement, place your child's back to a wall so that her shoulders touch, then side step along wall. Then, place child facing wall, tummy touching, walk side stepping;
- in varying tempos to a percussion instrument or a record;
- in various line patterns and pathways;
- pretending you are in the sand, mud, snow, on ice;
- around obstacles;
- holding hands with a partner.

Repeat appropriate activities with running movement.

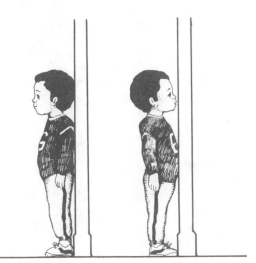

● Line or Rope Exploration

Make a line on the floor with a rope or masking tape. Ask your child to show you how she can
- jump over the line;
- walk along the line;
- stand on the end of the line;
- lie stretched out on the line;
- lie beside the line;
- walk, run, gallop around the line;
- roll over the line;
- cover the line with her body.

● Balance Beam

Have your child walk along a sturdy balance board (10 to 15 cm wide and 2.5 m long and not more than 50 cm off the ground). Encourage her to walk
- forward with hands stretched sideward for balance;
- sideward with hands stretched sideward for balance;
- forward to the middle of the board, turn and walk forward back to the same end;
- backward with the help, if needed, of an outstretched hand;
- forward and place a bean bag on the board, stand and continue walking to the end.
- over small obstacles; for example, bean bags or a shoe box placed on beam.

Note: It is better to teach these skills on the ground before performing them on the balance beam. A beginner or apprehensive child needs adult support.

● Throwing and Catching

○ Select a fairly large soft ball (nerf, fluff, beach ball) to begin practicing this activity. Face your child, 0.5 to 1 m apart, and gently lob the ball aiming at her outstretched arms. Encourage your child to squeeze or nestle the ball against her body. Praise and reinforce attempts to catch. Ask your child to throw the ball to you. Don't be discouraged if you spend more time chasing the ball than catching it.

○ Practice throwing accuracy by placing a large cardboard box 1 to 1.5 m away from your child. Give her some newspaper to make paper balls and encourage her to toss the ball into the box. Often, scrunching the newspaper into balls is more fun than throwing it. Bean bags, balls, spools, and other such objects can also be used.

○ Practice throwing accuracy by attaching a favourite character target on a wall at your child's eye level, 1 to 1.5 m in front of her. Practice throwing and hitting the target with a bean bag or soft ball. Encourage your child to retrieve it.

● Hitting and Batting

○ Suspend a ball, balloon, ball in mesh bag at your child's shoulder level. Encourage her to hit the ball with her right hand, left hand, and two hands.

○ Encourage your child to hit a suspended ball with a large bat, coat hanger bat or small paddle.

○ Encourage your child to hit a fluff ball, a plastic puck, or a large beach ball with a plastic hockey stick.

○ Purchase or make a batting tee. Place a large ball on top of the tee. Give your child a large bat and encourage her to grip the bat with two hands, standing on the side of and facing the tee in a position to bat the ball off the tee.

● Kicking

Provide your child with a large rubber ball she can kick against a wall, retrieve with two hands, and place on the ground for another kick. Repeat. When she masters this skill, increase the challenge by putting an interesting colourful target on the wall. Repeat action aiming at target. Encourage your child to use both the toe and instep of the foot.

● Ice Skating

Purchase a pair of ice skates that tightly attach to the child's boots. Place a protective helmet on head for safety purposes. From behind, support your child under the arms assisting with a gliding motion. As your child gains more confidence, she may wish to move holding on to a chair or two traffic cones, one for each hand. The child learns to walk balanced on ice skates while pushing the support object along with the feet movements.

● Apparatus Activities

○ Visit your local playground equipped with a climbing apparatus. Encourage your child to climb, crawl, balance, slide, and swing.

○ Purchase or build a climbing apparatus, equipped with swings, cargo nets, slides, ladders, and tunnels for your back yard.
○ Design an obstacle course with boxes, ropes, laundry baskets, and boards.

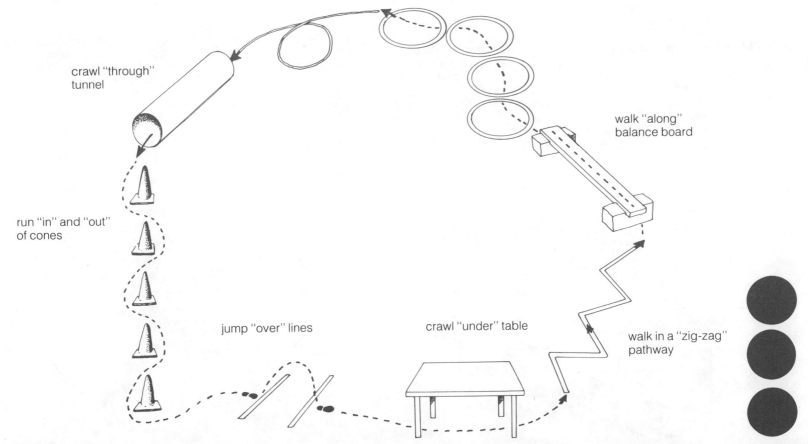

crawl "through" tunnel

run "in" and "out" of cones

jump "over" lines

crawl "under" table

walk "along" balance board

walk in a "zig-zag" pathway

● Water Play and Swimming

Swimming at this age is an enjoyable experience. If you can, enroll the child in "Parent and Me" swimming classes. Discuss the lessons with the child, watch other lessons, and take a small water toy to the lesson to "break the ice." Explore and play together.

● Building Super Structures

Provide the child with a variety of building materials, such as blocks, boxes, boards, blankets, chairs, rope, and other such materials. Encourage the child to build and create balancing objects with size and shape relationships.

● Blanket Explorations

Have your child select her favourite child-size blanket to
- be a big white *cloud* floating slowly over your house, your friend's house and through the park; vary speed of movement from slow to moderate;
- be a fierce *wind storm* twisting and whirling around. Your child should grasp the ends of the blanket firmly and make the sounds of the wind as she moves;
- to be a large *bird* flying high in the sky, flapping wings and diving up and down. Place the blanket behind the neck and firmly grasp blanket draped over outstretched hands;
- be a *ghost* moving and creeping around, uttering ghost sounds. Firmly grasp ends of blanket and let it fly above her head;
- enter a *dark cave* or *hole* and hide. Pull the blanket over body crouched in a small ball;
- *lie* on your favourite blanket and *rest*. Each child spreads her blanket on the floor and lies on it. This is a good time to perform some of the relaxation exercises described in the "You and Me Exercises" section;
- *fold* your blanket and *put it away*. This is a good opportunity to show your child how to fold. This activity develops eye-hand coordination.

● Carpet Square Fun

Give your child a carpet square (hoops or bicycle tire tubes are also good for this activity). Have her sit on the carpet square and encourage her to show you how she can
- walk around the carpet square;
- jump over the carpet square;
- run in and out of all the carpet squares lying on the floor. Run without touching the carpet squares;
- balance on her seat, shoulders, knees, and feet on the carpet square;

- sit down and stand up several times on the carpet square;
- run, touching only the carpet squares.
- balance on the carpet square touching the square with one hand and one foot; 1 foot, 2 hands; 2 feet, 2 hands; 1 hand and seat, etc.

● Rhythms, Music, and Dance

To the Mailbox
Your child carries a valentine, walking around in rhythm to the music. When the music stops, deliver the valentine to another person. She now becomes the new walker. This dance can also be enjoyed by changing movements at the end of each verse.

> I'm walking to the mailbox, the mail box, the mail box
> I'm walking to the mailbox, To mail my valentines
>
> I'm skipping to the mailbox . . . .
> I'm hopping to the mailbox . . . .
> I'm tiptoeing to the mailbox . . . .

Small and Tall
Play in partners or in a group in a circle. Your child covers her eyes while you both sing. At the end of the song, your child must guess who is standing tall or crouching down. If she guesses correctly, she has another turn.

> Sometimes I'm very, very small;
> Sometimes I'm very, very tall;
> Shut your eyes and turn around
> (adult turns child)
> And guess which I am now!

● Rhythmical Activities

Tommy Plays with One Hammer
To introduce stick tapping to rhythm, you and your child walk around the room together tapping rhythmically. Then, sing and tap to the following verse:

Tap, Tap, Tap around we go (walk, skip)
Tapping to and fro (tap sticks side to side)
Tap, Tap, way up high (over head)
Almost to the sky.

Variations:
Tap, Tap way down low
Tap, Tap very slow.

Pease Porridge
Adult and child face each other, clapping hands together to the exact rhythm of the words. In the beginning the child may need help clapping hands. Place your hand over child's and sing the song. Any variations to the clapping action is fun and enjoyable.

Pease porridge hot (hit partner's hands)
Pease porridge cold
Pease porridge in the pot
Nine days old (clap own hands together)
Some like it hot (hit partner's hands)
Some like it cold
Some like it in the pot
Nine days old (clap own hands together)

● Singing Rhymes

Teddy Bear
Teddy Bear, Teddy Bear, turn around
Teddy Bear, Teddy Bear, touch the ground
Teddy Bear, Teddy Bear, show your shoe
Teddy Bear, Teddy Bear, that will do.

Teddy Bear, Teddy Bear, go upstairs
Teddy Bear, Teddy Bear, say your prayers
Teddy Bear, Teddy Bear, switch off your light
Teddy Bear, Teddy Bear, say good night

Good night.

Jack be Nimble
Sing the rhyme "Jack by Nimble." On the word "over," jump over a shoe box, or on an imaginary candle.

Jack be nimble
Jack be quick
Jack jump "over"
The Candlestick.

Games

● Active Games for Two of You

Big Turtle
Using a mat or blanket, crawl under the mat, which acts as a turtle shell, and move it as a unit.

Big Ball Balance

Balance a beach ball between you and your child using different parts of your bodies (fore-heads, hips, elbows, knees) by putting pressure on the ball. If necessary, use your hands to help. Balloons and nerf balls are also suitable for this activity.

Freeze

Your child walks, runs, skips, or hops around the room. On the command "freeze", she stops and stands still on the spot. As she becomes more skilled, encourage her to make different shapes with her body.

Ring Toss

Secure an old bat on a wooden platform. Toss plastic rings, hoops, or inner tubes over post.

Bean Bag Basketball

Hold a square box at waist level, 1 metre in front of your child. Encourage child to throw one or several bean bags into box. Praise all attempts. Your turn next! Your child may need to stand on a sturdy low chair or wooden box to provide more challenge for you and to help you improve your basketball skills.

Partners

Ask child to hop, skip, run, and jump to music. When the music stops, you and your child join hands and then let go. Repeat several times. As skill improves, try joining elbows, touching hips, locking legs, or hugging when music stops.

● Passive Games for Two of You

Shape Sorting

Purchase a shape sorting toy. You can also make a shape sorter with coffee cans or ice cream containers. Cut shapes in cover of cans and make appropriate sized shaped objects to fit through holes in the cover.

Threading

Improve hand-eye coordination by giving your child a shoe lace, pipe cleaner, or blunt-ended needle to thread small objects such as buttons, macaroni pieces, or beads.

Manipulative Activities

Purchase Lego, Tinker Toys, puzzles, play dough, lacing cards, nesting toys, construction tool kits, and peg boards. Encourage experimentation for development of finger dexterity and hand-eye coordination.

● Active Games for Large Groups

Treasure Chest Pass

This game is designed to introduce young children to circle game-playing. Passing objects of different sizes and shapes assists in developing grasping and passing skills. Children form a circle by joining hands. Place a box full of objects varying in size, texture, and shape – a small ball, a large ball, a paddle, bean bag, rope, badminton bird, wooden spoon, fluff ball, can, rhythm bells in the centre of the circle. Pass the box around giving each child a treasure. Each child should talk about her treasure and return the treasure to the box. Place the box in the centre of the circle. Then one child selects an object. On the whistle "go" this child starts passing the object around the circle. On the whistle "stop," the child with the object exchanges it for another treasure. Repeat several times. As the children's skill and cooperation improves, play the same game to music.

Musical Carpet Squares

Each child takes a carpet square, finds a place on the floor, and sits on her carpet square. The adult plays a music to start and stop the actions. The children walk, run, skip, hop, slide, or jump around the area. When the music stops they must sit on the closest carpet square. Remove one or a few carpet squares each time the music stops. Encourage all children to share the few squares that remain. This game can also be played with hoops, pillows, small chairs, and adult's laps.

Move and Learn Games

This game is designed to combine learning and moving. The child can learn primary colours, numbers 1 to 5, animals, and shapes. Introduce only one concept at a time, reviewing the game several times before introducing a new concept. Select rubber-backed carpet pieces in blue, yellow, and red. Place several pieces of each colour on the floor. There should be enough colours for each child to stand on; that is 6 children, 6 red squares, 6 blue squares, 6 yellow squares. The children are asked to stand on their favourite colours. On the command, the children walk around the area. The adult calls "red" and holds up a piece of red construction paper. The children stand on a red quare. Repeat several times. As the children become more skilled, encourage them to share colour squares and remove the visual aid. Don't worry if some children do not stand on the correct colour. Point out a few children who do and continue the game. Many will just enjoy moving from square to square in the early stages.

The
Four
Year
Old

The four year old is an interesting and energetic child described by some experts as wild and wonderful. Adult wishes are recognized and yet, your child is now aware that his opinion counts as well. He respects parents and others. Boundaries, rules, and regulations are understood, but not always remembered. The child tries to impress upon others the behaviour he has learned. For example, he tries to encourage others to share and take turns.

Your child loves to please and boasts of accomplishments. Statements such as "I can climb higher than the house" are characteristic of this age group. He enjoys friends and considers anyone who shares experiences with him a friend — teacher, parent, neighbour, playmate. Siblings are loved and cared for by the four year old. However, moods change readily so reactions may be unpredictable. Emotions are expressed with demonstrable feeling. Outbursts of laughing or crying can often be changed by silly conversations. Your child cannot resist laughing when you react by saying "You're a silly billy" or "You're acting like a squishy marshmallow."

Your child loves all body movement for the simple joy of moving. Drive and energy appear endless. Movements are quick and calculated. He walks, runs, jumps, hops, gallops, crawls, climbs, throws, catches, and kicks with more efficiency. Fine motor skills have improved, and he can thread, lace, build, button, and pour with ease. Creative play and simple games are enjoyable activities. He needs to be provided with a variety of opportunities to demonstrate abilities and satisfy the intense inward drive to move.

A Four's Movement Abilities

The following movement abilities are presented as guidelines to help you determine the activities appropriate for this age group.

● Reaching, Grasping, Releasing, and Manipulating

Your four year old
- throws a ball with accuracy and is beginning to rotate his upper body when throwing;
- catches a large ball tossed from close by;
- bounces a large ball using two hands;
- hits a suspended ball with either or both hands, large bat, or paddle;
- hits an easily tossed well-aimed ball with a bat;
- builds complex structures with objects of various sizes and dimensions;
- kicks with inside of foot, harder, and further than before;
- kicks with some accuracy at a wall target;
- kicks to a partner and stops the moving ball with two hands before kicking.

● Sitting

He also
- sits and pedals a tricycle or a small two-wheeled bicycle with or without training wheels.

● Crawling and Climbing

Your four year old
- Climbs structures, ladders, slides, fences, and trees with a firm hand grip, good foot positioning, and controlled balance.

● Walking and Running

Your four year old
- walks and runs skillfully forward and backward, side steps and varies speeds, pathways, and levels
- walks on tip toes forward and backward;
- walks on the inside and outside of his foot;
- walks in time to music;
- walks up and down stairs with skill;
- walks skillfully on balancing apparatus, turns, and performs stunts;
- runs, starting and stopping with control;
- runs around obstacles;
- gallops changing feet;
- skips moving forward.

44

● Jumping

Your four year old
- jumps with increased skill while taking-off and landing;
- jumps over objects;
- jumps over heights;
- jumps in combination with walking or running;
- lands with balance, ankles and knees flexed and arms outstretched in front;
- hops on one foot unaided but not for long.

● Water Play and Swimming

Your four year old
- swims moving arms and kicking feet supported by adult, life jacket, or water wings;
- feels comfortable playing in water, jumping into adult's outstretched arms from the pool's edge, splashing, and blowing bubbles.

You and Me Exercises

Lazy-Day Rest
To relax the body.

Position: Lie on the floor with your legs slightly apart and arms placed limply at the side.

Action: Take a deep breath, hold, relax. Pull your toes towards and away from body, hold, relax. Pull tummies in, hold, relax. Tighten seats, hold, relax. Make a tight fist with hands, hold, relax. While hands are still at side, shrug shoulders, hold, relax. Smile while turning head from side to side. Frown and repeat action.

Small Ball
To relax the body and stretch the muscles.

Position: Kneel on the floor with your legs together.

Action: Rest your seats on your legs, lower your head to the floor, and tuck your hands to side on floor pointing backwards. Hold, relax.

Magician Sit
To relax and stretch muscles.

Position: Sit cross-legged on the floor, knees bent to side, soles of feet together, back straight.

Action: Gently lower your knees towards floor.
Variation: Gently lower your head towards floor.

Rockin' Rolls

To stretch the back and strengthen the abdominal muscles.

Position: Sit on the floor, knees bent, feet on floor and hands clasped together under knees. Head is tucked to knees.

Action: Rock gently on the back keeping body in tucked position. Do not rock back on shoulders as it is too difficult to continue rocking action.
Variation: Rock side to side.

Windmills

To strenthen chest and arm muscles.

Position: Stand with your feet apart and arms outstretched to your sides.

Action: Rotate your arms in small circles, gradually increasing the size of the circles. Change direction, action. Repeat gradually increasing the speed of rotation.

Jack-in-the-Box

To strengthen legs and total body stretch.

Position: Squat down with your hands on the floor.

Action: Jump up stretching your arms above your head. Repeat a few times.

Sit-up

To strengthen the abdomen.

Position: Lie flat on your backs with your knees up and feet flat on floor, your hands stretched above your heads.

Action: Gradually sit up and then slowly lower your bodies to starting position.

Forward Roll

To stretch muscles and increase coordination.

Position: Your child squats down on a mat or soft surface with arms on outside of legs and hands placed on the mat in front of him. Child lower his head so that his chin touches his chest, making his body very round. Remember fluff ball held under chin ensures a nice round back. There is no need to assist your child now during this action.

Action: Place back of head on mat and roll forward to sitting position.

Backward Roll

To stretch muscles and increase coordination.

Position: Your child squats down on a mat or soft surface with his back towards the mat. Place hands behind head with thumbs near the ears. Tuck chin to chest and bend head forward making body into round ball.

Action: Unaided, child rolls backward keeping body tucked. Push on mat with hands during roll-over. Finish in squat or kneeling position. This action is difficult and the child may not stay in rounded position, thus stopping action or rolling to one side over the shoulder.

Motor Development Activities

● **My Body**

Have your child identify the right and left sides of his body. Encourage him to remember which side is right and which side is left. References, such as the hand you use to colour and write or the hand you use to pick up your fork, are very helpful hints. Again, adults should stand beside or behind child when working on laterality, saying "show me how you can"

- ○ raise your right hand, lower your right hand;
- ○ touch your foot, knee, elbow, head with your right hand;
- ○ swing your right arm;
- ○ shake your right hand;
- ○ raise your right foot, lower your right foot;
- ○ move your right hip.
- ○ Repeat these activities using the left side of body.

Manipulate different objects with right and left hands; for example, squeeze a ball, pile up blocks or cans, hit a suspended ball or balloon, roll a ball, throw a bean bag.

Hold up parts of the body while standing, sitting, or lying down.

● **Rope Exploration**

Place a series of short ropes or masking tape lines on the floor. Encourage your child to follow the leader and run perpendicular to the lines taking one step between each rope. As your child become more skilled, increase the space between ropes to encourage larger strides.

Encourage your child to jump over a rope 15 cm high, balanced on a support at each end. If this is too threatening, let your child choose the height that is comfortable. Make sure the rope can be easily knocked down without harming your child.

With one end of a skipping rope in each hand, encourage your child to swing the rope back and forth and jump over it. If your child wants to, swing the rope over his head and try skipping; encourage this action.

Your child will enjoy playing and experimenting with skipping ropes in many different ways

o make shapes – circles, squares, letters – with rope and jump over, walk around, or get inside them;

o stretch rope lengthwise and walk, skip, run, jump, hop "along" or "over" rope;

o cover a rope outstretched on the floor with your body;

o balance while holding the rope in a variety of ways;

o swing and sway, pull and tug rope;

o have a tug-of-war between two or several persons;

o tie ropes together for a circular or square shape tug-of-war;

o play "Horsey" by placing a rope loosely around your child's tummy as your hold on to the "reins". Child leads. Reverse roles.

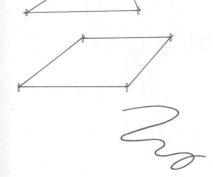

● Building Superstructures

Provide your child with a variety of building materials such as blocks, boxes, boards, blankets, chairs, ropes, and other such materials. Your child will enjoy creating structures, by balancing objects and draping blankets.

● Blanket Fun

49

Give your child a blanket or towel to

o be a big white *cloud* floating in the sky;

o be a fierce *tornado* or *hurricane* whirling and twirling around moving in a variety of ways;

o be a *ghost* under the blanket and moving about making ghost sounds;

o be a *bird*, flying and landing;

o enter a *dark cave* and hide from the monsters.

As a group activity several children grasp the edges of a blanket. Place a small light weight ball in the centre of the blanket. The children move the blanket to keep the ball popping like popcorn. As another group activity have several children sit and grasp the edges of a blanket. Sing Row, Row.
Row Your Boat; gently but rhythmically tug in one direction. then the other.

● Crawling and Climbing

Take a walk with your child and balance on rocks, ledges, lines, cracks, and boards. Visit a local playground equipped with a climbing apparatus which will inspire a variety of movements.

● Balancing Stunts

Select one or several of the following balancing apparatuses and encourage your child to practice balancing in a variety of ways.

Balance Beam
- ○ Walk, tip toe, turn, squat, step over bean bags.
- ○ Walk balancing an object in hands or on head.

Balance Board
- ○ Feet together, apart.
- ○ Arms in different positions.
- ○ Holding objects in hands.

Ladder Travel (ladder on floor)
Walk forward, backward between rungs; on rungs.
Walk with hands and feet between rungs; on rungs.
Walk forward straddling ladder, hop or jump between rungs.

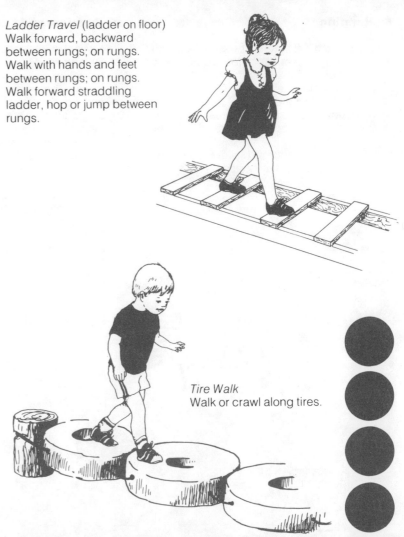

Rocker Board
o Sit, lie, kneel or stand on board and rock.
Caution: Keep fingers away from edge of board.

Tire Walk
Walk or crawl along tires.

Scooter Balance
o Stand and push scooter with one foot.

● Hopping

Demonstrate the difference between hopping and jumping. Ask your child to "show me how you can" hop
- on the right foot, left foot;
- forward, backward;
- over rope or masking tape lines placed on the floor close together;
- high and low.

Holding a child's hands may provide the support he needs to practice hopping.

● Jumping and Landing

Ask your child to "show me how you can jump"
- forward, landing on balls of the feet, bending ankles, knees and hips;
- forward, backward, sideward;
- and turn, landing in a balanced position;
- and reach for a suspended ball or balloon;
- over a line or rope;
- over a small low box;
- like popcorn popping;
- over several box hurdles placed on the ground in a row;
- like a kangaroo; rabbit;
- from various heights starting low and working up;
- forward off a box, landing with good control and balance inside a bicycle tire or hoop. Hoop is placed on the floor in front of the box.

● Kicking

Ask your child to "show me how you can kick"
- a large ball, stop with hands, and repeat;
- the ball high in the air;
- a ball at a large target placed 1 to 3 metres away;
- a ball between objects; for example, cones or carpet squares placed in a line;
- milk cartons over a standard around 1 metre high;
- a ball and try to knock down cartons, placed 1 to 2 metres away from your child.

● Throwing and Bouncing

The child can practice throwing skills by
- bouncing and throwing a large ball using two hands;
- catching a ball with an adult who is positioned 1 to 2 metres away;
- throwing a ball into an open cardboard box placed 1 to 2 metres away;
- throwing a ball at a target positioned 1 to 2 metres away from your child and at his eye level.
- throwing a ball or bean bag at varying levels, directions and speed;
- throwing a ball at cartons standing on a support; for example, balance beam placed at the child's eye level.

52

● Hitting and Batting

The child can practice hitting skills by
- batting a large ball off a stable batting tee;
- batting a tossed ball with a large bat. Encourage your child to hold a large bat in batting position. Stand 1 to 2 metres from your child and toss a fairly large rubber ball at his bat while your child swings to try to hit the ball;
- hitting a plastic puck or ball with a plastic hockey stick at a target; to a partner.

Note: Your child may become discouraged easily. If he seems apprehensive, stop the activity and practice another day.

● Water Play and Swimming

Your child is now beginning to feel more comfortable in the water. Although bathtub and wading pool water play is fun, he will now show interest in learning to swim. Your child should be comfortable in the water with you in his early years. If you and your child have taken "Parent and Me" classes, continue, and if he is ready try swim classes by himself. Discuss the possibility of taking swimming lessons. Visit the pool where the lessons will be taught. Watch other lessons in progress. Talk about the importance of learning to swim and reassure your child that you will be present at every lesson to support and encourage him. Watch attentively, as your child will feel more comfortable knowing you are present. After the lesson, praise his efforts. In only a few lessons, you will be amazed at his progress. All the effort and time spent orientating the child to the water in the early years paid off. Be proud of yourself!

● Roller Skating, Ice Skating

These activities are fun and challenging for the four year old who should wear a helmet and knee pads for safety. You can help by supporting him under the arms from behind.

● Singing Rhymes

The Bear Walked Over the Mountain
Sung to the tune of "For He's a Jolly Good Fellow."

The bear walked over the mountain
The bear walked over the mountain
The bear walked over the mountain
To see what he could see.

But all that he could see
But all that he could see
Was the other side of the mountain
The other side of the mountain
The other side of the mountain
Was all that he could see.
(Children and adult join hands and walk around in a circle)

So he ran to another mountain
He ran to another mountain
He ran to another mountain
To see what he could see.
(Turn around and run the other way)

But all that he could see . . . etc.

So he hopped, skipped, marched, tiptoed, climbed, jumped, clumped, stamped to another mountain (or whatever the child likes to suggest).

Looby Loo
During first verse, skip and circle around in a ring. In following verses, do the appropriate actions.

> Here we go Looby Loo
> Here we go Looby Light
> Here we go Looby Loo
> All on a Saturday night.
>
> You put your right foot in
> You put your right foot out
> You give your right foot a shake, shake, shake
> And turn yourself about.
>
> You put your left foot in, etc.
> You put your right hand in, etc.
> You put your left hand in, etc.
> You put your whole self in, etc.

Stretching
> Stretch, stretch, way up high
> Stretch, stretch, way down low
> Stretch to the right and stretch to the left
> And stretch in the way that you like best
> Yes stretch in the way that you like best.
>
> Twist, twist, round and round
> Sweep, down to the ground
> Sway to the right and sway to the left
> Then move in the way that you like best
> Yes, move in the way that you like best.

● Moving to Your Favourite Record

Moving to a favourite record is fun. Select a record and dance together. See the Music section in the References for appropriate records.

 # Games

● Active Games for Two or Three of You

Shuttle Race
Place two boxes 3 metres apart. Put several interesting objects in one of the boxes. On the signal "go", your child runs and takes an object from one box and places it in the other. Repeat until the box is empty. You may wish to talk about the objects in the box first, so his curiosity will not interfere with playing the game.

Sweep
Place the open end of a box towards the starting point 3 metres away. Give your child a broom or hockey stick to sweep or hit a ball or similar object into the box. Repeat several times.

Bean Bag Hit
Standing facing each other 3 metres apart. Place a large beach ball in the centre between you and your child. Each person has a bean bag and tries to move the ball by throwing the bean bag at it to the other person's side.

Magic Carpet Ride

Child grasps sides of a gym mat, towel, or piece of thick plastic, while sitting in the middle of the mat. You pull the carpet around the area. This works best on a tile floor. You can also hold child by the feet if he lies down and legs are in the air.

Note: This game can be varied to include several children with one child sitting in middle of mat and other children holding side and moving mat around. Adult assistance will be needed.

Long, Long, Long Jump

The object of the game is to jump together as far as you can. You broad jump first. Your child starts where your heels landed and broad jumps. Continue taking turns. How far can you jump working together?

Simon Says

Stand facing each other. Your child says "Simon says do this" and performs an action. Adult imitates. However, if your child says "Do this" you must not imitate action. If you do, you change roles.

● Passive Games for Two or Three of You

Number Shapes

To stretch muscles, increase balance and strengthen parts of the body, have your child form number shapes with his body. Diagram of these figures should be made to give visual clues. Attach examples to the floor or hold up for your child to view. The four-year old child does not know what they look like in various shapes so let him look in front of a large mirror so he can make his body the same shape as in the picture.

● Active Games for Large Groups

Squirrels-in-Trees
Scatter carpet squares or hoops around the playing area. Instruct children to stand on a carpet square. Tell them the squares are "trees" and they are the "squirrels". On a given signal, the squirrels must leave their tree and find a new one. Repeat action several times. Variations: Cut carpet pieces into different shapes. Repeat game, telling "squirrels" to find a specific shape. Sharing carpet shapes may be necessary.

Frozen Bean Bag
The children move freely, balancing a bean bag on their heads. As the children become more skilled, increase the speed of movement: skip, run or side step. If the bean bag falls off a child's head he is frozen and must wait for another child to place it back on the frozen player's head. Four year olds hold on to their own bean bag while assisting others.

● Parachute Games

Parachute games are exciting and provide opportunities for maximum participation and learning social and game skills. Purchase a parachute through your local sporting goods store or suggest that one be donated to your group by a sky-diving group. Parachutes are very expensive so several day care, nursery school, or preschool groups could purchase a parachute and share it. You can make a parachute by cutting out pie shaped pieces of nylon material and sewing them together in a circular shape. A hole in the centre is necessary to distribute air under the parachute.

Row Your Boat
Position: Sit down in a circle, firmly grasping the edges of the parachute.
Action: Tug and pull on edges of parachute in one direction and then the other. Sing "Row, row, row your boat, Gently down the stream. Merrily, merrily, merrily. Life is but a dream." The leader will need to designate which direction to tug and pull.

Waves
Position: Sit down in a circle, firmly grasping the edges of the parachute.
Action: Move parachute by lifting arms up and down making big and small waves.

Merry-go-Round

Position: Stand up, firmly grasping edges of the parachute.
Action: Walk in one direction and then the other. Pretend you are on a merry-go-round going faster and faster.

Old Red Wagon

Position: Stand up, firmly grasping the edges of the parachute.
Action: Walk and do the actions in the following song: Circle to the right, Old red wagon. Circle to the right, Old red wagon. Circle to the right, Old red wagon, Fare thee well my darling . . . Circle to the left . . . Into the centre/Out of the centre.

Up and Down

Position: Stand up, firmly grasping the edges of the parachute with the right hand. All children face and travel in one direction.
Action: Sing
   Ring around the Rosy,
   A pocket full of posies,
   Hush-a, Hush-a
   We all fall down (children hold parachute and fall down)

   Down in the garden
   Picking butter cups
   Along comes the bee
   Buz--z-z-z-z-z-z-z-z (flap parachute)
   And we all jump up (children hold parachute and jump up)

Glorious Fanning

Position: Stand up, firmly grasping the edges of the parachute and make waves by moving parachute up and down.

Action: Children go under parachute, lie flat and get a "glorious fanning" of breeze created by the parachute waves. Predesignate turns — boys then girls, or number children, 1, 2 — all the one's then all the two's go under.

Name Game

Position: Stand up, firmly grasping the edges of the parachute with two hands.

Action: Several children are chosen to go under the parachute and hide. When their name is sung, that child pops up through the hole in the parachute. Children sing the following song:

> Where is Michael?
> Where is Michael?
> Here he is! (Michael pops up through the hole)
> Here he is!
>
> How are you today, Sir? (bow)
> Very well, I thank you (Michael answers)
> Run and hide.
> Run and hide.

Popcorn

Position: Stand up, firmly grasping the edges of the parachute with two hands; make small and large waves.

Action: Place one, and then several light-weight balls of different shapes, colours and sizes on the parachute and move balls to and fro, keeping them on the parachute. Have children attempt to pass the ball from side to side while tipping the parachute.

Climb the Mountain

Position: Stand up, firmly grasping the edges of the parachute.

Action: Make a mountain by trapping air under the parachute, by lifting it high and bringing it down fast. After doing this several times, stop and explain that some of the children can climb the mountain by letting go of the parachute and crawling on top. Take turns climbing the mountain.

59

Off and Running

Throughout this booklet we have illustrated exercises, activities, and games for you and your child to enjoy together. You have watched your child walk, climb, run, hop, strike, kick, and move in a variety of different ways with increasing skill and confidence. You have had fun with your child while learning motor skills and becoming physically fit. You have imitated each other's movements and created games and exercises together. Although the child is maturing and wishes to play more on his own, he still needs your constant encouragement and support. So continue to share this special time together as he keeps on "moving and growing."

If you wish any further information on fitness for your child or yourself write to:

Fitness Canada
365 Laurier Avenue West
Ottawa, Ontario
K1A 0X6

References

● Motor Development

Ames, L.B. and L. Frances. *Your Four Year Old*. New York: Dell Press, 1976.

Ames, L.B. and L. Frances. *Your Three Year Old*. New York: Dell Press, 1976.

Bunker, Linda K., Cardine E. Johnson, and Jane E. Parker. *Motivating Kids Through Play*. West Point, N.Y.: Leisure Press, 1982. This publication is available in Canada through: Canadian Intramural Recreation Association, 333 River Road, Vanier, Ontario K1L 8H9.

Carbin, C.B. *A Textbook of Motor Development*. Dubuque, Iowa: Wm. C. Brown Co., 1980.

Dalley, M.L. "Diary of the Motor Development of Children: Birth to Three Years." Unpublished manuscript, Ottawa, 1980.

Dalley, M.L. "Diary of Motor Development of Children: Three to Six Years". Unpublished manuscript, Ottawa, 1981.

Espenschade, A.S. and Eckert, H.M. *Motor Development*. Columbus: Charles E. Merrill Books, 1967.

Gallahue, D.L. *Understanding Motor Development in Children*. Toronto: John Wiley and Sons, 1982.

Gallahue, D.L. *Developmental Movement Experiences for Children*. Toronto: John Wiley and Sons, 1982.

Lévy, J. *You and Your Toddler*. Toronto: Pantheon Books or Random House of Canada, 1980.

McClenaghan, B.A. and D.L. Gallahue. *Fundamental Movement: A Developmental and Remedial Approach*. Toronto: W.B. Saunders, 1978.

McDiarmid, N.J., M.A. Peterson and J.R. Sutherland. *Loving and Learning: Interacting With Your Child From Birth to Three*. Don Mills: Longmans Canada, 1975.

Roufberg, R.B. *Today He Can't – Tomorrow He Can! Your Child From Two to Five Years*. Vol. 2. New York: Foundation Publishing, 1971.

Stanford, D.J. *Guidelines for Parents and Teachers on Play and Physical Activity*. Dubuque, Iowa: Kendall, Hunt Publishing Co., 1982.

● You and Me Exercises, Activities and Games

Barr, B. *Exercise Games for Children and Parents*. New York: Drake, 1978.

Burton, E.C. *Physical Activities for the Developing Child*. Springfield: Charles C. Thomas, 1980.

Canadian Parks/Recreation Association. *Little Duffer Doo Time*! Nepean, Ontario: Canadian Parks/Recreation Association, 1980.

Cousineau, S. "Mom's and Tot's Exercise and Play Activities". Unpublished manuscript prepared for Kanata Community Programs, Kanata, Ontario, 1979.

Dalley, M.L. *Moving and Growing: Exercises and Activities for the First Two Years*. Ottawa: Fitness Canada and Canadian Institute of Child Health, 1983.

Doray, M. *J Is For Jump! Moving Into Language Skills*. Belmont, California: Pitman Learning, Inc., 1982.

Michaelis, B. and D. Michaelis. *Noncompetitive Activities and Play*, Learning Handbooks, 530 University Avenue, Palo Alto, California 94301, 1977.

Murphy, Chet. *A Parent's Guide: Teaching Kids to Play*. West Point, N.Y.; Leisure Press. This publication is available in Canada through Canadian Intraumural Recreation Association, 333 River Road, Vanier, Ontario K1L 8H9.

Murray, K. *Infaquatics, Teachings Kids to Swim*. New York: William Morrow and Co., 1980. This publication is available in Canada through Canadian Intramural Recreation Association, 333 River Road, Vanier, Ontario K1L 8H9.

Orlick, T. *The Cooperative Sports and Games Book: Challenge Without Competition*. New York: Pantheon Books, 1978.

Prudden, B. *How to Keep Your Child Fit From Birth to Six*. New York: Harper and Row, 1964.

Rasmus, C. and J. Fowler. *Movement Activities for Places and Spaces*. Washington, D.C. 20036: A.A.H.P.E.R., 1977.

Riggs, M.L. *Jump To Joy*. Englewood Cliffs, N.J.: Prentice-Hall Inc., 1980.

Riggs, M.J. *Movement Education for Pre-school Children*. Washington, D.C. 20036: A.A.H.P.E.R.D., 1980.

Schoedler, J. *Physical Skills for Young Children*. Toronto: Collier-MacMillan Co., 1973.

Shank, Carolyn. *A Child's Way to Water Play*. West Point, N.Y.: Leisure Press, 1983. This publication is available in Canada through the Canadian Intramural Recreation Association, 333 River Road, Vanier, Ontario K1L 8H9.

Sparling, J. and I. Lewis. *Learning Games for the First Three Years.* New York: Berkley Books, 1981.

Winters, S.J. *Creative Rhythmic Movement for Children of Elementary School Age*. Dubuque, Iowa: Wm. C. Brown, 1975.

Other Resources

● **General**

Canadian Institute of Child Health. *Where Do I Go For Help?* Ottawa: Canadian Institute of Child Health, 1982.
A directory of provincial, national and international organizations offering information and services related to the care of children. Available for $5.00 from the Canadian Institute of Child Health, 17 York Street, Ottawa, Ontario K1N 5S7.

Fitness Canada. *Fitness and Pregnancy*. Ottawa: Fitness Canada, 1982.
This booklet outlines a fitness program for the pregnant woman, including warm-up exercises, aerobics, and calisthenics. It also includes suggested postpartum exercises. Available free from Fitness Canada, 365 Laurier Avenue West, Ottawa, Ontario K1A 0X6.

Health Programs Branch, Health and Welfare Canada. *Up the Years from One to Six*. Published by the authority of the Honourable Marc Lalonde, Minister of National Health and Welfare, Ottawa, 1973.

Markum, P. *Play: Children's Business and a Guide to Play Materials*. Washington, D.C.: Association for Childhood Education International (ACEI), 3615 Wisconsin Avenue N.W., 1974.

Evaluation of play and its impact at various developmental levels. Lists play activities and appropriate play materials for children from infancy to eleven years.

Sutton-Smith, Brian and Shirley Sutton-Smith. *How to Play with Your Child and When Not To*. Toronto: Prentice-Hall, 1974.

The authors trace a child's development from birth to thirteen years and the kinds of activities he or she might be engaged in. They also offer suggestions to enhance and stimulate play. Parents will find this book particularly useful.

Watts, Harriet M. *How to Start Your Own Pre-school Playground*. New York: Universe Books, 1973.

Werner, P. and R. Simmons. *Inexpensive Physical Education Equipment for Children*. Minneapolis, Minnesota: Burgeo Publishing, 1976.

● **Safety**

Canadian Red Cross Society. *Be Sure They're Safe*. Toronto: Canadian Red Cross Society.
This pamphlet gives important "water safety wisdom" for parents.

Canadian Red Cross Society. *The Water in Your Back Yard*. Canadian Red Cross Society, Toronto.
An excellent information booklet on backyard pool safety.
Both of these are available from your local Red Cross Society or The Canadian Red Cross Society, 95 Wellesley Street East, Toronto, Ontario M4Y 1H6.

Canadian Toy Testing Council. *The Toy Report*. Ottawa: Tyrell Press Ltd., 1983.
This report lists recommended and not recommended toys for children of all ages based on comprehensive testing, reactions from children, and other research. Listings cover the age group for the toy, price range, and comments on why it is or isn't recommended. Available for $3.50 from the Canadian Toy Testing Council, P.O. Box 6014, Station J, Ottawa, Ontario K2A 1T1.

Consumer and Corporate Affairs. *Is Your Child Safe?* Ottawa: Consumer and Corporate Affairs, 1982.
This excellent booklet provides information to assist you in providing a safe environment for your child at home. It contains tips on buying toys, cribs, playpens, and pacifiers. Available free from Consumer and Corporate Affairs Canada, Communications Service, Hull, Québec K1A 0C9.

Consumers' Association of Canada. *Kids in Cars*. Ottawa: Consumers' Association of Canada, 1982.
This excellent booklet describes what kind of child restraint systems are available and detailed information on how to use them properly. Available for $2.00 from the Consumers' Association of Canada, Box 9300, Ottawa, Ontario K1G 3T9.

Fire Prevention Canada. *Burns Can Be Prevented*. Ottawa: Fiprecan.
A pamphlet including ways to prevent burns to children including hot tap water burns, hot liquids, and electrical hazards. Available free from your local fire department.

The Hospital for Sick Children. *Please Make My World Safe*. Toronto: The Hospital for Sick Children, 1980.
An excellent booklet concisely describing the most common causes of accidents to young children. Also describes ways to prevent them! Available free from The Medical Records Department, The Hospital for Sick Children, 555 University Avenue, Toronto, Ontario M5G 1X8.

Jones, Sandy. *Good Things for Babies*. Boston: Houghton Mifflin, 1980.
A sourcebook of safety and consumer advice for the first two years of baby's life, picturing over 150 items.

Maynard, Fredelle. ***"How to Childproof Your Home***. *Chatelaine* Vol. 56, No. 5 (June 1983).
A short, concise article with practical tips for childproofing. Fredelle takes a year by year approach for the first three years of the child's life.

Ontario Ministry of Health. **Accidental Poisoning: Prevention**. Ottawa: Health and Welfare Canada, 1982.
A kit on how to poison proof your home. Takes a room-by-room approach.

Transport Canada. **Keep Them Safe**. Ottawa: Department of Supply and Services, 1982.
A booklet describing safe use of automobile child restraint systems. Available free from Transport Canada, Ottawa, Ontario K1A 0N5.

● **Music**

Beall, Pamela and Susan Ripps. **Wee Sing and Play: Musical Games and Rhymes for Children**. Los Angeles: Price-Stern-Sloan Publishers Inc., 1981.

Beall, Pamella and Susan Ripps. **Wee Sing: Children's Songs and Fingerplay**. Los Angeles: Price-Stern-Sloan Publishers, Inc., 1981.
Two delightful booklets of musical games and rhymes for young children.

Forte, Imogene and John MacKenzie. **Try Squiggles and Squirms and Wiggly Worms**. Nashville. Incentive Publications, 1978.
A creative movement book for the very young child. This book is to be read "with" not "to" the child, allowing him/her to learn through experimentation and creative involvement.

Move Along Alphabet: A Teaching Tool for Basic Involvement, Kimcho Educ., 0510.
These two records can be used as an accompaniment to the book *J is for Jump*. Each album includes one 12" record and a teacher's guide. Price $10.50 each. Order from Maya Doray, 666 West End Avenue, New York, N.Y. 10025.

Records

Raffi, Troubadour Records:
Singable Songs for the Very Young;
More Singable Songs;
The Corner Grocery Store.

Sharon, Lois & Bram, Elephant Records:
Smorgasbord;
One Elephant, Deux Elephants;
Schoolyard;
Singing and Swinging.

Suzanne Pinel, Les Productions Marc Ltée:
Je m'appelle Marie-Soleil, Bonjour!
Un cadeau pour toi.

Sesame Street, Sesame Street Productions:
Sesame Street Disco;
What Time is It.

Anne Murray, Capital Records:
There's a hippo in my tub.

Pat Carfa, A & M Records:
Lullabies and laughter with the Lullaby Lady.